Nursery Rhymes

Higgledy, Piggledy
My Black Hen

Higgledy, Piggledy.
My black hen.
She lays eggs for gentlemen;
Sometimes nine, and sometimes ten.
Higgledy, Piggledy,
My black hen!

Little Boy Blue

Little Boy Blue, come blow your horn;
The sheep's in the meadow,
the cow's in the corn.
"Where's the little boy that
looks after the sheep?"
"He's under the haystack, fast asleep."

Bow Wow Wow
Whose Dog Art Thou?

Bow, wow, wow
Whose dog art thou?
Little Tom Tinker's dog,
Bow, wow, wow.

Baa, Baa, Black Sheep

Baa, baa black sheep, have you any wool?
Yes sir, yes sir, three bags full;
One for my master, one for my dame,
And one for the little boy that lives in our lane.

There was a Crooked Man

There was a crooked man, and he went a crooked mile;
He found a crooked sixpence against a crooked stile;
He bought a crooked cat, which caught a crooked mouse,
And they all lived together in a little crooked house.

Diddle Diddle Dumpling

Diddle, diddle, dumpling, my son John
Went to bed with his stockings on:
One shoe off and one shoe on.
Diddle, diddle, dumpling, my son John.

Hickory, Dickory, Dock

Hickory, dickory, dock
The mouse ran up the clock.
The clock struck one,
The mouse ran down.
Hickory, dickory, dock.

Jack and Jill

Jack and Jill went up the hill
To fetch a pail of water;
Jack fell down and broke his crown,
And Jill came tumbling after.

Jack Be Nimble

Jack be nimble, Jack be quick,
Jack jumped over the candlestick.

Three Little Kittens

Three little kittens
Lost their mittens;
And they began to cry,
"Oh! Mother dear,
We really fear
That we have lost our mittens."
"Lost your mittens!
You naughty kittens!
Then you shall have no pie."
"Mee-ow, mee-ow, mee-ow."
"No, you shall have no pie."
Mee-ow, mee-ow, mee-ow.
Mee-ow."

Mary, Mary Quite Contrary

Mary, Mary, quite contrary,
How does your garden grow?
Silver bells and cockleshells,
And pretty maids all in a row.

Little Miss Muffet

Little Miss Muffet
Sat on a tuffet,
Eating her curds and whey;
Along came a spider,
And sat down beside her,
And frightened Miss Muffet away.

Old Mother Hubbard

Old Mother Hubbard
Went to the cupboard
To get her poor dog a bone;
But when she came there
The cupboard was bare,
And so the poor dog had none.

Pat a Cake

Pat-a-cake, pat-a-cake, baker's man!
Bake me a cake as fast as you can;
Prick it and pat it, and mark it with a T,
And put it in the oven for Teddy and me.

Peter Piper

Peter Piper picked a peck of pickled peppers;
A peck of pickled peppers Peter Piper picked;
If Peter Piper picked a peck of pickled peppers,
Where's the peck of pickled peppers Peter Piper picked?

Pussy Cat Pussy Cat Where Have You Been

"Pussy-cat, pussy-cat, where have you been?"
"I've been up to London to look at the queen."
"Pussy-cat, pussy-cat, what did you do there?"
"I frightened a little mouse under the chair."

Queen of Hearts

The Queen of Hearts,
She made some tarts,
All on a summer's day;
The Knave of Hearts,
He stole those tarts,
And took them clean away.

Rock A Bye Baby

Rock-a-bye baby, in the tree top;
When the wind blows, the cradle will rock;
When the bough breaks, the cradle will fall;
Down will come baby, cradle and all.

Sing a Song of Sixpence

Sing a song of sixpence.
A pocket full of rye,
Four and twenty blackbirds
Baked in a pie.
When the pie was opened,
The birds began to sing;
Wasn't that a dainty dish
To set before the king?

Twinkle, Twinkle, Little Star

Twinkle, twinkle, little star;
How I wonder what you are!
Up above the world so high,
Like a diamond in the sky.
When the glorious sun is set,
When the grass with dew is wet.
Then you show your little light,
Twinkle, twinkle, all the night.